THE AGE OF REPTILES

Iguanodon

THE AGE OF REPTILES

Life in Prehistoric Times

By DOROTHY E. SHUTTLESWORTH

Illustrated by Matthew Kalmenoff

GARDEN CITY BOOKS, GARDEN CITY, NEW YORK

Sauropod *Polacanthus* (above) *Ornithocheirus* *Dragonfly*

FOR GREGORY
who likes to look into the distant future
as well as at the remote past

The author's sincere appreciation goes to Dr. Edwin H. Colbert, curator of fossil reptiles and amphibians at the American Museum of Natural History, for his kindness in reading this manuscript and giving the benefit of his valued criticism

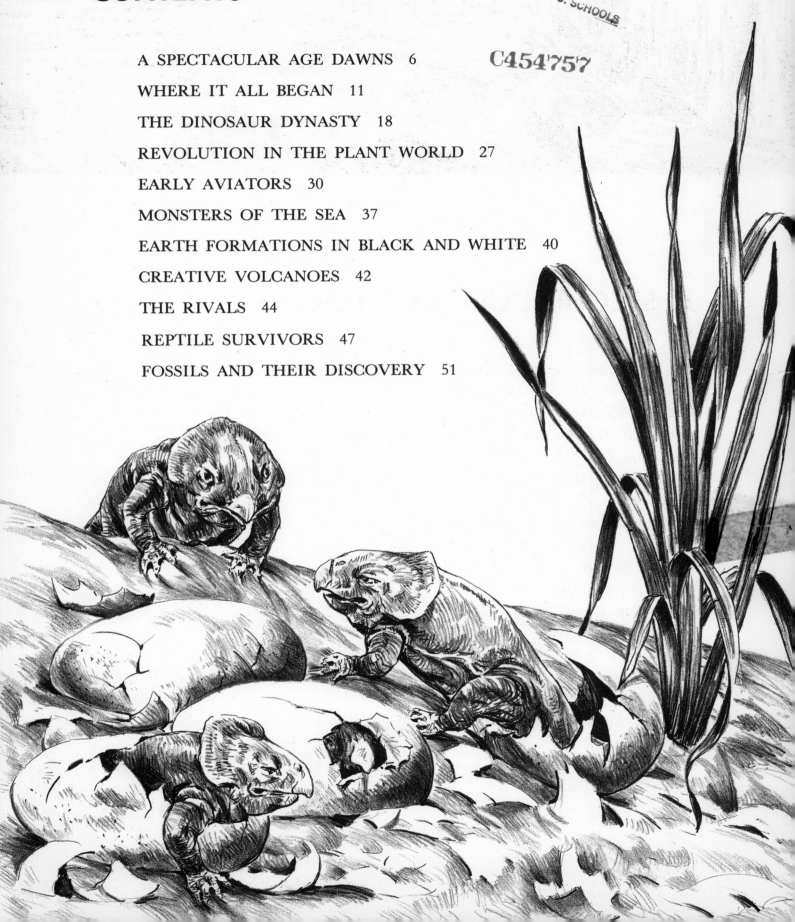

CONTENTS

A SPECTACULAR AGE DAWNS

The rise and fall of the mighty dinosaurs is an endlessly fascinating story. Under what circumstances did they become established? What conditions caused some of them to grow to the gigantic size of a locomotive? And since they were so huge and powerful, why did they disappear from the earth?

Because they did not survive, dinosaurs sometimes are considered "unsuccessful." But the fact is, the Age of Reptiles, during which dinosaurs rose to top importance in the animal world, lasted *one hundred and forty million years.* The Age of Mammals, which followed, was a mere seventy million. Man has lived on earth far less than one million years. When these figures are considered, we realize the dinosaurs did very well in making their mark in the earth's history! The span of time during which they lived is scientifically named the Mesozoic era, but this era is popularly called the Age of Reptiles and also the Age of Dinosaurs.

During a hundred and forty million years many, many changes can take place. And change the world did, not only in its reptile life but in other kinds of animals and plants, as well as in climate and in the shapes of continents and oceans. However, the developments during this

6

time were not so drastic when compared with those that took place in the comparatively short period known as the "Permian" which came just before the reptilian age. It was then that vast areas of rock were thrust out of the earth to form the Appalachian Mountains—a range extending more than two thousand miles. As the Appalachians rose, there was also a gentle uplifting of the entire eastern portion of North America, as well as considerable volcanic activity, and the outlines taken by this part of the earth assumed the form which, on the whole, they have kept ever since. To the west huge inland areas were gradually disappearing, so that when the reptilian age dawned our entire continent, except for swamps, lakes, and rivers, had emerged as a dry area. Volcanic activity, especially along the coast from California to Alaska, brought further changes to the land. This program of change was not confined to North America, but was being carried on in other parts of the world as well.

As land and water areas shifted on a grand scale, weather conditions also changed drastically. Changes in ocean currents helped to determine local climates, and some regions even in the Southern Hemisphere were quite frigid, while other areas baked in relentless heat until they became parched deserts. We can easily imagine how plants and animals must have suffered as the conditions under which they lived changed from hot to cold and from wet to dry, or the other way around. But at last the Permian period came to a close and the new era began, bringing more even climates and less violent earth changes—and life was ready to carry on in ever greater variety and abundance.

Diadectes

It was during the Permian that reptiles began to take an important place in the earth's population. They were primitive in nature, but hardy enough to survive rigorous times and to establish the dinosaurs, which we look upon with wonder and considerable admiration. One of the primitive group, a three-foot-long lizard-like creature known as *Seymouria*, has been termed "grandfather of the reptiles," for in structure it was basically like all reptiles that came later. However, as with other primitive reptiles, it was in so many ways like an amphibian it is considered a link between the two forms of life.

Seymouria (so named because of fossil remains discovered near the town of Seymour in Texas) lived only in North America, but close relatives inhabited Europe. Its descendants branched into two general divisions, one remaining small, the other having a tendency to grow to gigantic size. *Labidosaurus* was one of the small descendants. Like its noted ancestor, it had an elongated body and weak limbs. Also, as with *Seymouria*, its teeth were sharp-pointed spikes—very efficient for catching and eating other animals. *Labidosaurus* also was equipped with a hooked upper jaw, which is, in fact, responsible for its name. Taken from the Greek, *labio* (*labidos*) is "forceps" and *sauros* is "lizard."

A more sizable descendant living in North America was *Diadectes*. Though five or six feet in length, this creature still had the sprawling legs of its ancestor and therefore must have been most awkward on its feet. But it did not have to worry about speed in chasing prey for it apparently was a plant-eater. Its teeth were blunt, more like pegs than like spikes. Russia in Permian times was the setting in which *Scutosaurus* flourished. Here was a primitive reptile as large as an ox! With a head small in proportion to the body, legs that bowed outward, and a generally ungraceful form, *Scutosaurus* was an ungainly monster indeed. Closely related reptiles, also of large size, lived in South Africa as well as in Europe. Seemingly all were nourished by plant life and were sluggish in their movements.

8

A group of reptiles that spanned the end of the Permian period and the early part of the reptilian age had a characteristic lower opening in the skull roof behind the eye. The most picturesque of this group were those which had a great "sail" attached along the back. *Dimetrodon* was one. Though about the same size as *Diadectes*, he was a far less desirable neighbor to other animals for he had numerous sharp, dagger-like teeth and was an active hunter. With his sail rising two or three feet above his backbone, he must have presented a terrifying sight as he pursued his victims. Sometimes these victims were other sail-bearing reptiles, such as *Edaphosaurus*. This had the same advantage of six-foot size, and it strongly resembled *Dimetrodon* in other ways, but it lacked teeth suitable for fighting or eating flesh. Both these animals disappeared, however, by the close of the Permian period.

Edaphosaurus

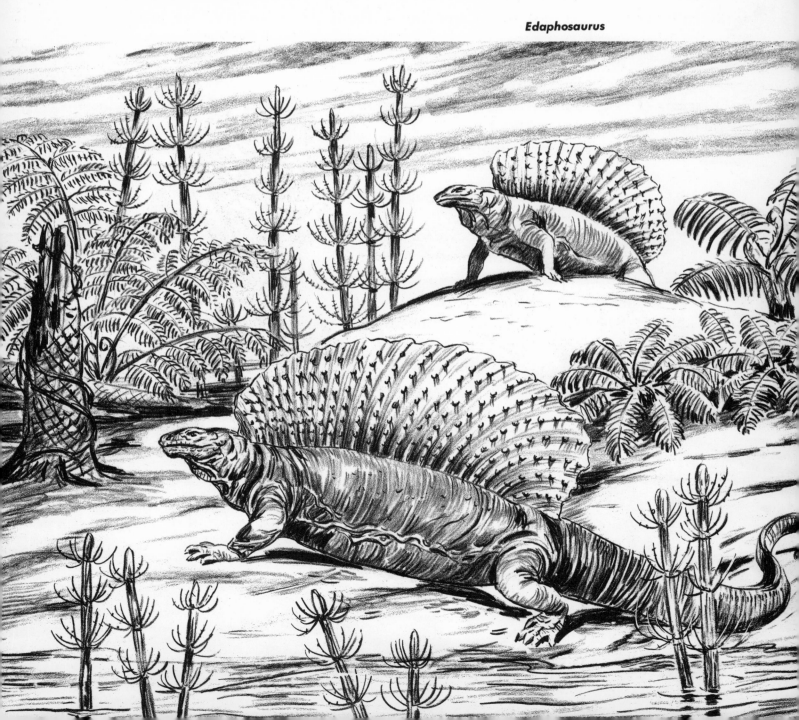

Very different in looks was *Moschops*, one of a number of large plant-eating reptiles with particularly strong limbs. Its back sloped sharply, giving it the appearance of "sitting up" when it actually was standing on all fours. *Moschops* had rather weak jaws and peg-like teeth— indications that it, too, was a vegetarian. The large, heavy, primitive reptiles like *Moschops* (which also disappeared by the close of the Permian) helped to populate Africa and Europe before dinosaurs made their appearance.

As the Permian gave way to the Triassic period—the first of three great periods in the Age of Reptiles—important new characters appeared in the reptilian drama. But before making their acquaintance let us look at still earlier days for the full scope of change that had taken place since the miracle of life on earth began.

Moschops

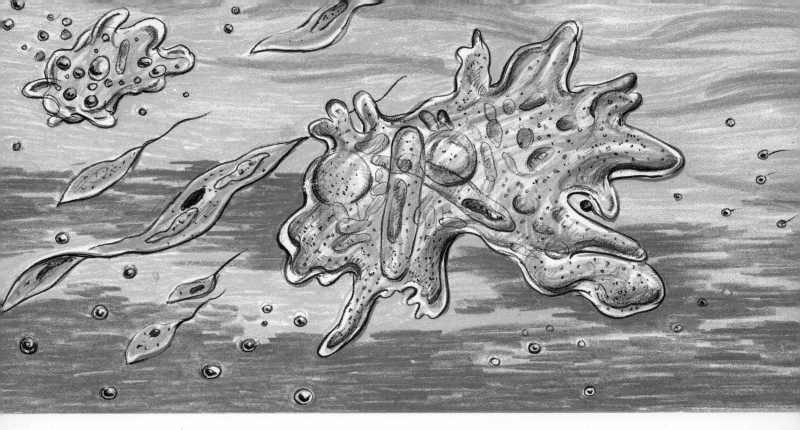

Amoeba

WHERE IT ALL BEGAN

Long before there were primitive reptiles, long before amphibians and fish existed, life was stirring in the coastal waters that washed against barren rocks. Still earlier there had been nothing but solid rocky earth, sandy deserts, and water. Activity was limited to rain, winds that drove sand and water before them, and the thunderous upsurging of volcanoes.

Against this bleak and violent setting a story began its first chapter quietly. Had anyone existed to observe what was going on, he might have thought the story of little importance, especially as he would have needed powerful microscopes to see any part of it! Its earliest characters were probably the tiny organisms known as Protista ("the very first")—the simplest of life-forms which cannot be classed definitely as plant or animal. The drama of life moved slowly but at last reached a second chapter when these single life-forms gave rise to two different groups. Now one-celled creatures similar to our modern amoeba populated the water and Protophyta ("first plants") floated alongside them.

11

Further unfolding of the story's plot came with descent to the sea floor of some of the little swimming creatures and floating plants. Here the new surroundings led to new habits of life. Some of the animals attached themselves to the mud, and from then on their only movement was to wave about on stems. Others developed the ability to travel over the sea floor, using considerable effort to push themselves along. Then there was another development that was to "leave its mark" in more ways than one, for this concerned the appearance of shells. These hard coverings gave the creatures that wore them valuable protection, and because in the ever increasing population a race for survival had begun, this was important. For humans who were to come much later, shells were important because they were hard—something that might last in a fossilized state. History was being recorded in a way that could be understood millions of years after the time the shells were being worn by living animals.

As shells became the fashion, the earth story grew far more complicated. Not only were there such soft creatures as jellyfish and worms, but a variety of echinoderms (creatures with spiny skins, such as the modern starfish), molluscs (shellfish, such as present-day oysters and snails), and arthropods (animals with jointed feet—forerunners of such as the lobster). Altogether there was a tremendous variety of animals without backbones, each variety differing enough from the others to be given a scientific classification of its own. The Age of Invertebrates was under way.

Outstanding in this prehistoric scene were the trilobites. Sometimes it is said that they in their day, like the dinosaurs in theirs, were "rulers of the earth." However, this is only because of their vast numbers. In appearance they were not impressive, like the reptiles. Their average length was no more than a couple of inches; an exceptional species measured two feet. They lived mostly in shallow water, prowling about the sea floor on crab-like legs in search of food. Many kinds preyed upon other animals and were able to burrow for worms as well as catch small swimming creatures, while others thrived on seaweed or decaying vegetable matter. The trilobite was an odd sort of swimmer; it was as apt to travel upside down as right side up and to move backward instead of forward. Its body was designed in threes—the shell which covered it was divided into three distinct lobes by furrows which ran from front to back. The body itself was divided into three parts: a strong shield at the front and another at the rear, and a soft middle section. This middle was made up of small sections which could move against each other until actually rolled into a ball.

Dinichthys, a fish giant

The Age of Invertebrates wore on, and at last into the watery scene something really new was added. Certain animals came into existence which had a slim rod of gristle running the length of the body. Here was the beginning of a backbone! The next step is easy to imagine: true backbones developed, and the invertebrates no longer had the world to themselves. The early underwater vertebrates were really fantastic. Many were armored. One type was covered with plates of bone on head and body, and even had thick rounded scales on its tail and bone-covered fins. On some, bony horns projected from the plating which covered the head.

Such armor gave fine protection to its wearers, but the "bone-heads" were definitely handicapped in swimming because of their bulk and weight. An improvement in the situation finally came with primitive fish that were smaller and less heavily armored than the others. These vertebrates changed in many ways to become more efficient and adaptable to various conditions, but probably the biggest improvement so far as influencing world history was concerned had to do with breathing. Certain types developed a lung which they used in addition to gills. It enabled them to obtain oxygen by gulping air through the mouth. The advantage of this feature was ability to survive during drought. If lakes and streams were drying up, fishes so equipped could often hold out until rains came again.

13

Trilobites   *Crinoids*   *Squid*   *Lampshell*   *Jellyfish*

                                                  Snail   *Starfish*

Another important aid developed on certain of the fish was the "lobe fin." Fishes so equipped had two pairs of fringe-like fins, each attached to a thick base or lobe. These were controlled by strong muscles, and might very well have served as primitive legs.

While these tremendous developments were taking place in the animal kingdom, plants also had been making great progress. Once completely dependent on the waters in which they came into existence, little by little they had been freed of this dependence. Countless numbers of them had been washed upon the shores, where they quickly withered and died from lack of moisture. But now and then one that was stronger than the rest survived until the tide turned again and brought it renewed vigor. In time certain plants not only found a way to survive at the water's edge but actually were thriving there. They sent roots into the soil and stiffened their stems, so that they stood upright even when not supported by water. Thus land plants came on the prehistoric scene—and the stage was set for the kind of animals we know as amphibians. Food awaited any "land lubbers" that might come along.

The first fish to struggle along dry land on their sturdy lobe fins probably were in quest of water to take the place of some that had dried up. However, they must have experimented in eating along the way, and as this proved successful their expeditions were extended longer and farther. As time rolled on, the muscular lobes increased in length and strength until they were more legs than fins.

Eusthenopteron (a lobe-finned fish)

It might seem that animals now designed for taking all needed oxygen directly from the air and having the ability to walk were ready to desert watery surroundings forever. But the break with their first home was still not complete; they had to return to water to lay eggs. The young depended on gills for breathing, and through infancy they had to live as fishes. Thus the word "amphibian," which means "double-living," is well suited to this group of water babies which turned into land-living adults.

The early amphibians flourished, increasing not only in numbers but in variety. Some became swift-moving and could even climb tree trunks, others stayed close to muddy ponds and were slow and sluggish. Their size ranged from an inch in length to a mighty ten feet. Many developed the type of skin which covers our present-day amphibians, the frogs and toads. Others had overlapping scales or a simpler type of armor. There was a great variety of shapes, although the usual type of head was broad and flat, with a wide mouth. However, some heads were long and came to a point. A tail was a feature on all, and all types had external nostrils. And for the first time in the already lengthy history of animals, openings in the head which might be called "external ears" came into existence. There were new sounds to be heard, also, for certain of the amphibians had tongues and were the first creatures to be "vocal."

As change followed change in the amphibian family, other developments continued in the seas and on land. The plant world particularly was flourishing. Instead of reproducing their kind by simple spores, many plants found an improved method in true seeds. Giant club-moss trees, or lycopods, grew abundantly. There were also the graceful cordaites, forerunners of later-day firs and pines, and handsome calamites with bamboo-like stems. Impressive as were these three kinds of trees, they were far outnumbered by ferns. These smaller green plants, in many varied shapes, formed a dense undergrowth—a perfect setting for all manner of creeping, walking creatures.

Our imaginary observer of the earth's unfolding drama might well think it had settled into a lasting routine, for it now looked well clothed and populated, and making a living was comparatively easy. But such was not the case. Changes of one sort or another were constantly occurring, especially in the Northern Hemisphere, where earth movements were slowly lifting former sea beds into swampy plains. Then came the Permian—the period of twenty-five million years when drastic changes were to test severely the survival ability of all living things. And it was then that little *Seymouria* and other primitive reptiles became prominent among the earth's creatures.

17

Cacops, an early amphibian

THE DINOSAUR DYNASTY

The contrast between the amphibians and the reptiles would not have looked so tremendous as that between fish and creatures able to live on land, for there was not a great difference in the general appearance or habits of adult amphibians and reptiles. The important development that had taken place concerned their eggs. Since amphibian eggs, like those of a fish, cannot survive exposure to air, the amphibians are never entirely independent of water. The reptile newcomer produced a type of egg with a protective tough shell and a yolk to nourish the embryo, so that the gill stage of a young reptile might be passed inside the shell. Therefore reptiles could wander over dry land with complete freedom; there was no need to stay in the vicinity of lakes or streams. Less noticeable than the change in egg-laying habits but still of real importance was a different kind of bone structure that was slowly evolving.

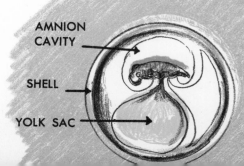

AMNION CAVITY

SHELL

YOLK SAC

Saltoposuchus

We have already met a number of the primitive reptiles that were part of the animal population during the Permian period. With the dawn of the Mesozoic era, which followed, life on land and in the seas progressed at a livelier pace. And as the era progressed it was soon apparent that in the new order of things reptiles had won first place in importance. The ancestor of all reptiles had appeared in the Permian; now came certain of its descendants which in themselves would also be famous "ancestors." Let us look at them—the thecodonts.

One that is characteristic of all primitive thecodonts was *Saltoposuchus*, a four-foot-long creature that lived in Europe. In contrast to those of the many reptiles that walked on four feet, its two hind legs had developed to a point where they could support the body unaided. Also there was a change in the hip joint, where the movements of the whole body were pivoted, and the hip girdle, or pelvis, gained increased strength. Creatures with this form could rise up on their hind limbs and *run*. A long tail did well for balancing the body as the two front limbs dwindled until they were used as hands rather than legs and feet. A narrow, deep skull formed the head of *Saltoposuchus* and other thecodonts, and it was equipped with teeth for eating flesh.

19

The thecodonts gave rise to several important kinds of reptiles, including the flying reptiles that came later in the Mesozoic era, the dinosaurs—and all crocodilians that have survived to this day. Among the dinosaurs there is a seemingly endless variety. Small, large, two-legged, four-legged, meat-eating, plant-eating, all these characteristics can be found among them, for "dinosaur" is a very general term. Actually it includes two great orders of reptiles, one being distinguished by typical reptilian hips, the other by hips similar to those of a bird in bone arrangement. The thecodonts became established early in the Triassic period. Later in the Triassic and by the next two periods, the Jurassic and the Cretaceous, both types of dinosaur were flourishing to an extent that truly made them the leading characters on the earth's stage.

Where would we look in the prehistoric scene for dinosaurs? Every continent had its share. North America was the home of many kinds from the small, rather helpless type to the fierce giant *Tyrannosaurus*. During the Jurassic period a lively little fellow here was *Ornitholestes*. No more than five or six feet in length (including a long, tapered tail) he had birdlike hind legs on which he probably could run rather swiftly. His front limbs were useful in another way. Small, with long claws which served as fingers, he could grasp his prey and efficiently hold it to his mouth. With sharp teeth he was well equipped to devour flesh, and his diet probably consisted of reptiles as well as eggs and small victims such as insects. He may also have been able to catch an occasional bird (a form of life that was just beginning in the Jurassic), and it is from this possibility that his name was created: *Ornis* is Greek for "bird;" *lestes* for "robber."

Ornitholestes

All in all, *Ornitholestes* closely resembled his thecodont ancestors. And he had a relative named *Allosaurus*, also living in Jurassic times, which was like him in certain ways. *Allosaurus* walked on two feet rather than four and also was a flesh-eater. However, *Allosaurus* was a giant. With body and tail thirty-five feet in length, his hind legs had developed enormously to support his great weight. His front limbs, which were hands rather than legs and feet, had claws like terrible iron hooks. His head was suitably large for the mighty body and the huge jaws were well supplied with strong, sharp teeth.

Allosaurus

Another giant North American dinosaur of the Jurassic period was *Brontosaurus*, the "thunder lizard." In fact its seventy- to eighty-foot length made *Allosaurus* seem small! The bulky body weighed many tons and was supported by four huge limbs, those in the rear being particularly large and massive. With *Brontosaurus*, and with certain other dinosaurs, we now see this change from the thecodonts: they are four-footed, having forsaken the two-legged stance. In spite of his four strong legs, *Brontosaurus* probably found walking very difficult. At any rate, he spent most of his days in swamps or in the shallows of lakes and rivers, where water helped in holding up his bulky frame. Another advantage of watery surroundings was that they helped keep at a distance flesh-eating enemies such as *Allosaurus*. The giant *Brontosaurus* himself ate only plants. His teeth were even and spoon-shaped—ill suited for tearing flesh.

Closely related to this beast was *Diplodocus*, the longest of all dinosaurs. He was not so bulky as *Brontosaurus*, but grew almost ninety feet in length! Much of this length was in the slender neck that supported a remarkably small head. He also was an animal of low, swamp lands, where marsh plants furnished abundant food.

Stegosaurus was a picturesque neighbor of these creatures, but lived closer to *Allosaurus* than to the swamp dwellers. Like the swamp dwellers, he stood on four legs and lived on plants; however, unlike them, he had equipment with which to defend himself against a faster-moving flesh-eater such as *Allosaurus*. A series of bony plates, triangular in shape and standing upright all along a steeply curved back, and a thick hide presented a discouraging surface for any flesh-eater to attack. Besides, there were four huge spikes on the tail which could be swung against an enemy.

Brontosaurus   **Stegosaurus**

Trachodon   **Tyrannosaurus**

After some thirty-five million years the Jurassic gave way to the third and last period of the Mesozoic era when seas expanded over land areas in many parts of the world. A great number of Jurassic dinosaurs vanished with the changing times, but one that managed to bridge the gap was *Camptosaurus*. He was not a giant; in fact he was rather small. In the front of his jaws he had no teeth at all; farther back there were rows of teeth suited for plant-chewing only. He moved about on large hind legs, but could come down on all fours when it seemed desirable to do so.

Despite all the variety in dinosaurs that had existed for millions of years, the Cretaceous period was to produce still different styles, as well as some that clearly were "new models" of the same old dinosaur. In Europe, for example, *Iguanodon* lived in much the manner of his somewhat earlier relative, *Camptosaurus*. He was fairly large. When he walked in an upright position, which he did much of the time, his head was about fifteen feet from the ground. He was very much at home in water, for the front of the skull and jaws was flat and broad, very well suited for groveling in mud and shallow water.

Another product of Cretaceous times was *Trachodon*. Here again the skull was flattened in front to form a giant "duck bill." Teeth were missing at the front of the "bill," but well over a thousand of them formed rows to the rear of the jaws. This was a semi-aquatic creature, in this case living along the rivers and lake shores of North America. Feeding on water plants and perhaps some shellfish kept *Trachodon* in water much of the time, and he would scurry there from dry land to escape a hungry flesh-eater. *Trachodon* in effect was an overgrown camptosaur.

23

Far from the American scene, on the plains of Asia's Mongolia, a small dinosaur was developing something new. The translation of its name indicates what this something was: *Protoceratops* is taken from the Greek, *protos* ("first"), *keratos* ("horn"), and *ops* ("face"). Actually the bump that grew on his nose was not much of a horn, but it was the beginning of an important feature. In years to come, on descendants far and wide, this would have developed into a strong fighting weapon. *Protoceratops* was no more than five or six feet in length, but had a most impressive head. This was large and deep, with jaws and muzzle forming a great hooked beak and back of the skull extending over neck and shoulders like a giant frill of bone.

The scene shifts around the world, again to North America, and time has moved on a tremendous number of years. Now we see a big lumbering beast about twenty-five feet long. His wide head is extended out over the neck in a great, bony shield which suggests an overgrown *Protoceratops*. And where the smaller reptile had the slight beginnings of a horn on his nose, this creature has one that is sturdy and of large size. Nor is it the only weapon on his head; over each eye is a sharp horn more than three feet long. This is *Triceratops* (meaning "three-horned-face").

Protoceratops

Triceratops   **Tyrannosaurus**

Triceratops was a descendant of the "first-horned-face" of Asia, and he had developed in more ways than size and additional horns. His neck and leg muscles were tremendous, and he had a ball-and-socket joint by which his great skull was attached to his backbone. Thus equipped he probably could lower his head until the long horns were directed at a target and then bring his head up with a deadly thrust. However, like his distant ancestor, *Triceratops* lived on plant life rather than preying on other animals. He kept his fighting abilities for an occasional male-against-male battle for supremacy—and to defend himself against *Tyrannosaurus rex*.

25

Here is a name which, translated, tells a real story: "tyrant king of the dinosaurs." *Tyrannosaurus* was just that. In size he was second to none of all creatures of his time. His head was eighteen feet above the ground. His body was fifty feet in length, topped by a head more than four feet long. In the enormous jaws were rows of dagger-like, six-inch-long, double-edged teeth. His heavy tail not only served as a prop when he was resting, but was a mighty club for fighting. Thus equipped *Tyrannosaurus* had little difficulty subduing almost any fellow reptile he chose to eat—and flesh was the only food he wanted. Despite the weight of his tail, it was never dragged as he ran but was carried off the ground, thus serving as a balancing weight for his great body. When *Tyrannosaurus* caught a victim he seized it with front legs which looked more like shriveled arms than legs and tore it to bits with hooked claws.

One dinosaur which was not especially bothered by the tyrant was *Ankylosaurus*. This armored beast did not have such fighting equipment as *Triceratops;* his only weapon was a club formed by his heavy tail which ended in a mass of bone. His advantage lay in an armor of bony plates fitted edge to edge like flagstones in a terrace. Since his entire body, head, and tail were covered by this heavy casing, even the teeth of *Tyrannosaurus* could not very well get at his soft flesh. He lumbered about the Cretaceous scene on all fours, undisturbed by the struggles going on between the great meat-eating reptiles and others not so fortunate as to have his remarkable armor.

These are but a few of the dinosaurs. Many close relatives of those we have been looking at, as well as others that were quite different, populated the earth during the Age of Reptiles. They seemed all-powerful, highly successful, and destined to last forever.

Ankylosaurus

Maple   Elm   Willow   Oak   Poplar   Conifer

REVOLUTION IN THE PLANT WORLD

About the middle period of the age of dinosaurs a revolution was begun, but it was in the plant kingdom rather than among the animals. The "revolt" was against the old-fashioned method of producing seeds, and it was carried out by the first true flowering plants.

When the Age of Reptiles began, plants had come a long way from their first attempts to sink roots into dry land. As we have seen, by the time invertebrates were well established in the seas, plants of many shapes and sizes were flourishing out of water. These included a great variety of

Sigillaria   Cordaites   Calamites   Lepidodendron   Protolepidodendron

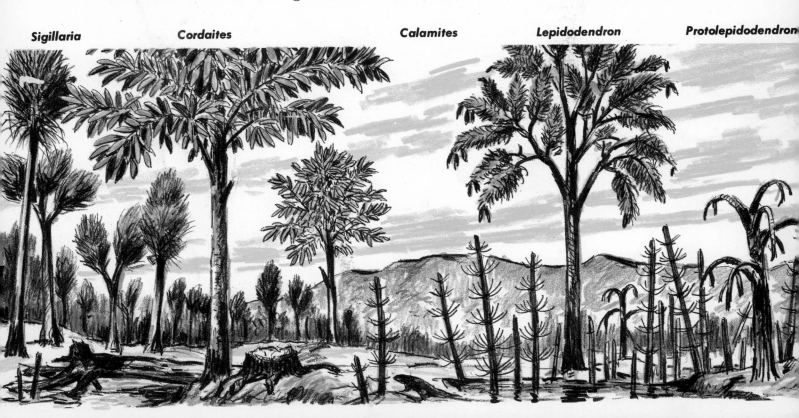

ferns. By the Permian period there were many types that grew close to the ground as well as tree ferns reaching sixty or seventy feet in height. There were also fern-like plants with foliage closely resembling the ferns but differing in that they developed seeds instead of spores. There were the huge cone-bearing scale trees, tall slender cordaites, and rush-like calamites. For millions of years before the Permian the mild temperature which prevailed over much of the world caused vegetation to prosper. Then in certain areas came the change to intense cold, and for plants as well as animals the struggle for existence became difficult indeed. Many did not survive, and by the Triassic period, which ushered in the Age of Reptiles, there was a great change in the character and distribution of plants.

A late Triassic landscape would show no familiar calamites or cordaites, but a number of "new" plants would claim our attention. Prominent by then were the cycads, a type that was to remain outstanding as long as dinosaurs trod the earth. Palm-like in general effect, the cycads had many varieties. With some the trunks were more like roots—they did not rise even slightly above the ground. With others the trunks were twenty, fifty, or even sixty feet tall. The leaves, too, differed greatly. On one type (*Sphenozamites*) a leaf was from three to four feet or more in length and from sixteen to twenty inches in width. It was composed of a woody leaf-stalk half an inch in diameter, with huge leaflets branching off its upper portion. These were blunt or "square-cut" at the tips, but at the base, where they joined the leaf-stalk, they curved into a sharp point. Another cycad (*Ctenophyllum*) was quite different in leaf style. Instead of being broad, its leaflets

28

grew to twelve inches in length, though only half an inch wide. Quantities of these extended from either side of the leaf-stalk.

So numerous and widespread over the earth were cycads during the Jurassic that this period is sometimes called the Age of Cycads, but there were also abundant ferns and conifers, including pines, cypresses, sequoias, and junipers. Scale-mosses, algae, lycopods, and small horsetails also helped make up the landscape, but were a less important part of it. Widely distributed was a tree that would look entirely familiar in modern times—the ginkgo. It is also known as the maidenhair tree because of the resemblance of its leaves to the maidenhair fern.

It was when the Jurassic gave way to the third and last period of the Age of Reptiles—the Cretaceous—that the "revolution" erupted with the appearance of true flowering plants. There was more reason than changing climates for vegetation to undergo changes: the shifting of land and sea areas had considerable bearing on plant life. At this time all continents were comparatively low-lying and in many places shallow seas extended widely over land masses. On our own continent much of the area that is now interior California and Oregon was flooded, and somewhat later seas spread over a broad belt from Cape Cod to Texas, and from the Gulf of Mexico to the Arctic Ocean. The effect was to divide the continent into two parts. Then by the close of the Cretaceous period these regions were elevated again. Thus plants of the lowlands often had to struggle against overwhelming difficulties. It was in the uplands that the true flowering plants arose. Today we know such plants as "angiosperms." They develop seeds in a closed capsule, or ovary—a contrast to both the spore-bearing plants and others which produce seeds but which do not give them the benefit of a closed covering.

The first angiosperms were hardwood trees—oaks, elms, willows, poplars, laurels, and magnolias were a few of them. Once established, the angiosperms continued to flourish with amazing success, and they were soon to outnumber the older types (the gymnosperms) in overwhelming proportions. Because of the generally widespread mild climate, the range of the hardwoods was great. It is probable many originated in the north—even as far as Greenland—and made their way southward.

Long before, an advanced type of egg had started reptiles on a career that was to become far more important than that achieved by the amphibians. Now the production of true seeds in a closed capsule started a new type of plant on a successful conquest of the world.

EARLY AVIATORS

With all the activity that had developed on land and in the sea, early in the Age of Reptiles the realm of the air was quite neglected and there was no such thing as a bird. Flight was first attempted by some of the invertebrates—the winged insects. A number of this six-legged tribe had made an appearance millions of years before, undoubtedly having developed from certain sea-dwelling animals. As the fateful Permian period began, they were numerous and varied. Outstanding were the cockroaches—all of four inches in length—and dragonflies with a wing-spread well over two feet. Insects may have had a setback during the Permian years, but by the middle of the reptilian age they populated the earth in vast hordes. Besides the dragonflies and cockroaches there were beetles, cicadas, grasshoppers, locusts, ants, and termites. Then butterflies and wasps appeared. Here was good flying material—and flight that was to prove of tremendous importance to the green earth, for insects flitting from plant to plant conveyed pollen and thus aided fertilization.

It was not until the Age of Reptiles was millions of years old that a vertebrate took to the air. And this first vertebrate aviator was not a bird but a flying reptile. Like the dinosaurs, the flying reptiles were descended from the thecodonts. The power of flight must have come gradually. We may picture certain reptiles crawling up trees, perhaps in pursuit of insects, then leaping from trunk to ground. The leaps grow longer, more frequent. In time descendants of the "leapers" develop tough, flexible membranes which spread from the sides of the body to the limbs. This is equipment for efficient gliding. As more time passes, the membranes increase in size and so does the strength of the muscles controlling them. A "wing" has been achieved.

With the development of wings, another aid to flight had been in the making. The bones of the reptile became hollow and filled with air, and large cavities were formed in the skull. The result was an extremely light-weight body.

(Flying reptile) *Pteranodon*   *Tylosaurus*

Dragonfly   **Cockroach**

Once flying reptiles, or pterosaurs, were established they flourished for something like a hundred million years—soaring over the heads of the lumbering earth-bound dinosaurs. They varied in size from a few inches in length to some with a wing-spread of twenty-five feet. There were long-tailed and short-tailed species.

By the Cretaceous period a real giant had come upon the scene. This was *Pteranodon*. With a head about six feet long and a wing-spread of at least twenty-five feet, he appeared to be lord of the air, as *Tyrannosaurus* was of the land. He was not a thing of beauty, having bare, smooth skin and an enormous beak. On land he was awkward for he had no equipment suitable for walking, and if he stood on his hind legs his great wings would have to be held up. Probably he made use of the "knuckle" joints on his wings, hooking himself to rock or cliff or tree. From such an anchorage he could launch himself into the air with a strong shove. *Pteranodon* depended on his eyesight, which was keen, rather than on his sense of smell, which was poor. This was a logical development since his hunting largely concerned fish, which he would spot from high in the air before swooping down for a catch.

Archaeopteryx

Long before *Pteranodon* was an important member of the animal kingdom, another vertebrate had taken to the airways. Like the flying reptiles, this was a descendant of the thecodonts, and in many ways there was little difference in the two kinds of animals. The skulls were very similar in form, as was the long tail each possessed. Both had a goodly supply of teeth. However, there was one important difference: the reptile had bare skin, the other creature wore feathers. Here was the first bird! The name given this early aviator is *Archaeopteryx* (translated "ancient wing").

Archaeopteryx was not completely clothed in feathers as are the birds we know today; small scales covered part of his body. But along the entire length of his forelimbs were rows of feathers placed where they would be of especial aid in flight. Feathers were to prove of value in another respect also: they would help to keep an even body temperature. This tied in with another important contrast between bird and reptile. Reptiles were (as they are today) cold-blooded: that is, their blood temperature—and therefore the temperature of the body—varies according to the temperature of their surroundings. With *Archaeopteryx* changes had been taking place in the circulatory system and in the structure of the heart which combined to make him warm-blooded, so that his body temperature remained constant. Thus if temperatures rose or fell drastically within a short period of time the bird was better able to withstand the change.

Probably much of this early bird's prey was made up of insects and small reptiles, and he must have pursued many of them on the ground or scrambling up trees. But there were also huge dragonflies to catch on the wing and no doubt *Archaeopteryx* captured his share. His teeth were also excellent weapons for seizing and holding prey, for they were widely spaced and sharp, and they slanted backward. Probably they were of little use in chewing.

In spite of his many advantages little *Archaeopteryx*—he was about the size of a crow—did not survive as long as the flying reptiles. By the Cretaceous period when *Tyrannosaurus* stalked the earth and *Pteranodon* sailed through the air, *Archaeopteryx* had vanished, but fortunately some of his descendants had become established. Strangely enough, one of the outstanding members of the feathered tribe had lost the power of flight! *Hesperornis* was a large bird, standing four or five feet high and having a big head with a long beak. His body was completely streamlined—no wings broke its smooth lines. The small remains of what once had been flying aids were buried under his thick coat of feathers. Walking must have been almost as impossible for him as flight, for his legs were very close to the tail and the heavy body was not balanced for action on land. Water was better. *Hesperornis* could paddle slowly or swim swiftly after fish. His family may have been raised on a floating nest made up of dead

Hesperornis

plants and mud, attached to rushes in shallow water, or at a location on shore to which the swimming birds could wriggle.

Ichthyornis was another fish-eating bird that was part of the Cretaceous scene. But although it could swim and it pursued prey in the water as *Hesperornis* did, it also could fly. Its wings and feet were very similar to those of birds of the present day. *Ichthyornis* was about ten inches long and to a considerable degree it resembled a bird known as the tern, which inhabits many shore areas.

Apparently it was toward the end of the reptilian age that birds began to exchange teeth and jaws for horny beaks. Other important changes were also taking place. We notice the disappearance of the long, jointed tail such as *Archaeopteryx* wore and the development of a shorter style in which the feathers could be closed or spread out like a fan. With *Archaeopteryx* the "fingers" which formed the framework of the wing were long and separate from each other. Gradually this was being changed until the finger bones were fused together and the wing surface was made up of stiff primary feathers. Also a fusion of bones in the pelvis made it an extremely strong and rigid structure. These developments laid the groundwork for a real success story, for despite the changes in surroundings that were to come in future years the birds flourished and became adapted to all sorts of conditions.

Ichthyornis

Ichthyosaurs   **Belemnites**

MONSTERS OF THE SEA

As reptiles soar through the air and wander far and wide over the land, let us investigate again what events are taking place in the seas. When we last looked at this realm, vertebrates in the form of fishes had joined the vast horde of invertebrates. Now we find added to these two groups another type of vertebrate—the reptile. Here is exhibited not so much a "chain" of events as a "circle." Life had started in the water, had slowly developed into land-living creatures we call reptiles, and now reptiles were back among the fishes!

Perhaps certain reptiles started invading the seas because they found food more easily there, or perhaps they did so to escape enemies. Whatever the reason, they began to adjust themselves gradually but quite completely to these different surroundings. They learned to swim, and some traveled through the water as swiftly and easily as the fishes. In some, legs were altered into flippers or paddles while others developed a strong fish-like tail as a swimming aid. Probably certain of them produced living young rather than laying eggs. In one important respect, however, the sea-dwelling reptiles did not change—they continued to use lungs for breathing air. They did not revert to gills.

At the dawn of the reptilian age several kinds of primitive reptiles had already begun a return to the sea, and during the Mesozoic era certain sea reptiles became huge, mighty, and altogether spectacular. One fish-like type we know as the ichthyosaurs. The body of an ichthyosaur was streamlined from pointed snout to tail tip and tapered gracefully from thick forward part to the rear. It might have a length of thirty feet, though many were far smaller. What once had been limbs were re-shaped into fin-like flippers. A large single fin along the back gave balance, so that the creature did not roll from side to side as he swam. The ichthyosaur truly gave the appearance of a fish, but bones, heart, and lungs were all reptilian. His eyes were tremendously large, his jaws long and lined with rows of sharp teeth. All in all, he was efficiently equipped for hunting in the water. The name ichthyosaur, meaning "fish lizard," suits him well.

The plesiosaur, another water-living reptile, was far larger than the ichthyosaur; his barrel-shaped body and snake-like neck might measure up to fifty feet. And there were other noticeable differences between the two. A plesiosaur's body was broad and flattened and his limbs, instead of being fin-like in appearance, more closely resembled oars. He used them like oars, too, paddling along close to the water's surface in pursuit of fishes. It was not necessary for his body to move swiftly in this hunting, for his long neck could rapidly dart far to either side and his jaws close on his victims before they suspected he was in their vicinity.

A fierce and monstrous rival of the plesiosaurs were the mosasaurs —a suitable name, for its translation is "sea lizards." And of all the mosasaurs, one of the most notable was the giant *Tylosaurus*, which swam through the shallow sea that covered large areas of western North America. He was equal in bulk to many of the dinosaurs, but being favored with an elongated, flexible body and a long, strong tail, he could give a good imitation of a fish in swimming. His paddle-shaped limbs, adapted from the legs and feet with which his remote ancestors had once walked on land, were useful aids in this locomotion.

As *Tyrannosaurus* was a terrifying hunter of the land, with his great size and dagger-like teeth, so the size and teeth of *Tylosaurus* made him a fearful hunter of the seas. Not only were his teeth large, numerous, and sharp-pointed, but his great jaws were hinged in the middle so that they

Plesiosaurs

Archelon

could be bowed outward. This made it possible for his mouth to open to take in extremely large victims!

One marine reptile that would seem very familiar to our modern eyes was *Archelon*, a tremendous turtle that inhabited the Cretaceous seas. He was all of twelve feet in length and must have weighed at least three tons. But *Archelon's* shell was light and soft, and he was not designed for the fast motion of *Tylosaurus* and some of the other water-living reptiles. As a result, the great turtles must oftentimes been used as a meal by their ferocious neighbors. *Archelon* had serviceable jaws himself, and a large parrot-like beak. With these he could munch on shellfish, which were abundant in the shallower seas where he lived.

Still another familiar reptile that swam in Mesozoic seas was a marine crocodile. In the later part of Jurassic times crocodiles were quite common in the waters of Europe. Later in the Mesozoic era they reached a size comparable to the giant *Tylosaurus*, but by then they had somewhat deserted the open waters for estuaries and the lower reaches of large rivers. Here they had frequent opportunities to feast on unwary dinosaurs.

The Age of Reptiles was truly an age of giants. And as giant battled giant it was proved that size was not all-important. Many other factors entered into the problem of survival, not the least of which was the behavior of the earth itself.

39

EARTH FORMATIONS IN BLACK AND WHITE

Toward the end of the Mesozoic era there were drastic adjustments in the earth: Ocean basins deepened to such an extent that shallow seas which had extended over continental areas drained into them. The large seas of western North America vanished and the Rocky Mountains slowly began to upraise where much of the waters had been. Mountain-building was taking place in other parts of the world, too, as in South America, where the mighty Cordilleras began to rise.

One important result of these changes was the formation of coal in tremendous amounts. This was not something new; many millions of years before, lush tropical forests had begun to be transformed into the dark, hardened mass of decayed vegetable matter that we know as coal. But coal-making is not confined to any period of the earth's history, and the Mesozoic seas were a great help in causing vegetation to decay. Earth pressures then finished the job of turning vegetation into hard black rock, and many new coal beds were laid.

Other deposits being formed in impressive quantities at the same period were white rather than black. One type was salt. As a shallow sea lost its outlet to the ocean, it grew saltier. The salt content was steadily increased by streams that carried into it various salts dissolved from rocks and soil. In time a period of drought completely evaporated the moisture of the "stranded" sea, and a thick salt deposit resulted.

Another "white" formation being created was a very fine type of limestone made from an accumulation of sediments rich in marine plants and animal skeletons containing quantities of calcium. Much of the earth's limestone-chalk was laid down during the last period of the Age of Reptiles. In fact the name of this period—the Cretaceous—was chosen because of the Latin word *creta*, meaning "chalk." It was first applied to the strata represented by the beautiful white cliffs of Dover and other formations along the English Channel. Great chalk deposits were also laid in this period on our own continent in areas that are now Kansas, Texas, and Alabama.

While it is true that most of the great chalk deposits were formed during the Cretaceous, other developments of equal or even greater importance were taking place at this time. As a result, "chalk age" is not a truly accurate description. However, the name has been used for so long that it is generally accepted. In somewhat the same way "Triassic" is not an appropriate name for the first part of the Mesozoic. It was chosen because the geologists who first studied rock strata from this period found it could conveniently be divided into three layers, and *trias* is Greek for "three." Even though later studies revealed not all Triassic rock had three layers, the name was retained. The Jurassic period was named for the Jura Mountains in Switzerland and France, where rock formations of that time were carefully studied.

CREATIVE VOLCANOES

By the Mesozoic era the eruption of volcanoes was an old, old story; they had been belching forth their fiery lava since the early days of the earth's history. During the Mesozoic they continued to be active, and to create some very remarkable and special kinds of land. One of these is the island which breaks through an ocean's surface and which in time may become inhabited by plant and animal life. Some of the most famed of volcanic islands are those that lie in the South Pacific, including the Hawaiian group. Actually they are the peaks of a great chain of mountains whose bases lie under fifteen thousand feet of water. With continuing eruptions they gradually built until they rose above the ocean's surface and established a series of dry land areas. Scientists have not agreed as to just when this happened, but we do know that it was begun millions of years ago and that some of the volcanoes in the Hawaiian chain are still active. One of them, Mauna Loa, erupts every few years but seldom does much damage. It obtains relief from the pressure of great internal heat by discharging enormous quantities of lava through a side fissure. Thus the molten stream can glide harmlessly into the sea, adding a bit to the size of the island rather than tearing it down.

As a result of their isolated situation, such islands did not have the same kind of plant and animal development as other lands. There existed no connection with a continent over which living things could migrate. But in time some seeds and spores were carried there by winds and birds, and vegetation made a start.

Around the world from the Pacific volcanic action was developing the rugged rock formation known as the Palisades which today borders the Hudson River. It was early in the reptilian age that this volcanic rock broke through to the surface. In British Columbia and extending into Alaska a number of volcanoes were also spreading vast quantities of lava which would endure as hard rock. In Africa molten rock was forming large plateaus, and in India two hundred thousand square miles were thickly blanketed with lava.

Although new islands were making an appearance and new rock was being formed, there was a rather drastic disappearance of land during the Mesozoic era. A submergence in southern Asia and northern Africa brought the Indian Ocean into existence. Land that had joined Australia to the southeastern end of Asia disappeared beneath Pacific waters and the "island continent" was formed. And it is believed that a broad land mass may once have extended between Africa and South America and that it, too, sank beneath ocean waves during this era.

By the end of the Mesozoic, planet Earth had indeed undergone remodeling on a gigantic scale. And, so far as general settings were concerned, it was on the threshold of modern times.

Cynognathus   *Cockroach*

THE RIVALS

Because of *Tyrannosaurus*, *Brontosaurus*, and other huge reptiles, it seems that the Mesozoic was an era of giants only. And certainly the enormous beasts do overshadow all lesser animals as we look at those days. However, very early in the reptilian age there appeared a new kind of creature which was unimpressive in size but whose prospects for the future were far brighter than those of the dinosaurs. We know it as the mammal.

The forerunners of the mammals had made a start in Permian times. They were cold-blooded and in their habits were true reptiles. But in structure—backbone, shoulder blades, hip bones, limbs, and feet—a change had begun from the reptile pattern. Also there was a change in the teeth. In most reptiles the teeth of any individual are more or less of the same peg-like pattern. But in the mammal-like reptiles there was definite variety in the teeth: in the front they were small and designed for grasping and nipping; back of them were a longer type well adapted for tearing and chewing.

By the time the Permian period had given way to the Triassic, there was a member of the mammal-like group so well developed that it merits

44

the name *Cynognathus*, or "dog-jaws," (from the Greek, *kyon, kynos*, "dog," and *gnathus*, "jaws"). This dog-jawed reptile which lived in South Africa was one of a group of reptiles that had strong legs which supported the body well off the ground and a long, rather dog-like skull. *Cynognathus* was no more than five feet in length, but he was built for quick action and could pursue his prey with rapid strides. Much as he resembled the mammals, however, "dog-jaw" could not be considered one of them; rather he was a link between them and the reptiles. By the end of the Triassic period he and his kind had passed out of existence, but into the picture by this time had come the first true mammals.

How difficult it would be to recognize these first of the "higher vertebrates" for what they were! For the most part they lived in trees or underbrush, and their food was largely seeds, fruits, insects, and probably the eggs of small reptiles and birds. Probably they did not produce living young, but laid eggs. However, when the babies emerged they were not left entirely to their own devices, as happened with reptile young. Tiny and undeveloped, they attached themselves to the mother's abdomen, where milk poured out to them through widely scattered pores. Years later when the mammals definitely were producing living young, their newborn babies still were so undeveloped they were completely dependent for life on the mother. For a while they lived in a pouch which covered her abdomen, where milk was supplied them through nipples—a definite advance from when the milk simply oozed out of pores. These pouched mammals, or marsupials, were a flourishing group by the close of the Mesozoic era, and they continue to be represented on earth until the present day. For the most part, however, they are restricted to Australia. On this island continent also are the only survivors of the egg-laying mammals: the duck-billed platypus and the spiny ant-eater.

It is easily seen that the unimpressive beginning made by these two groups of primitive mammals was only a small part of the mammalian story. Still during the reptilian age, a third class, the placentals, entered the race for survival. Not only did this type of creature bear living young, but produced babies that had a degree of independence from the beginning. Nevertheless, the mother took responsibility for their well-being. She nourished them with her milk and gave them a certain amount of protection. With these advantages combined with the others nature had bestowed—a warm-blooded constitution and hair or fur—the

45

placentals were on the way to a great future, destined not only to rival the reptiles but to surpass them in the conquest of the world.

The mammals' success did not come suddenly; the change-over in importance went on during millions of years. The first mammals had to be wary of the savage reptiles and try to keep out of their way. It was not until the Mesozoic era with its outstanding citizens, the dinosaurs, was a thing of the past that the hairy, warm-blooded beasts became numerous and increased in size. Now an Age of Mammals was in progress with a wonderful variety of beasts. Graceful little fellows about the size of a fox terrier, having three toes on the hind feet and four on the front, scampered about the woods and plains of North America. They are notable for having been the forerunners of our modern horse, and we call them by the name *Eohippus*, or "dawn horse." In Africa another creature no more than two feet high at the shoulder, with a strangely elongated upper lip, had become established. Its descendants were to roam far and wide and to alter greatly in form until the mighty elephant was achieved.

Far larger than ancestor of either horse or elephant was *Uintatherium*, which was a neighbor of *Eohippus*. This monster looked as frightening as some of the ferocious dinosaurs, being huge in size and carrying six horns on his head. He was not a hunter of other animals, however; like the horse and elephant ancestors, he ate only vegetation.

Along with these and many other plant-eaters, a variety of flesh-eating mammals were flourishing. Slowly but surely the mammalian tribe gained ground, and the reptiles took a place of far less importance as citizens of the world.

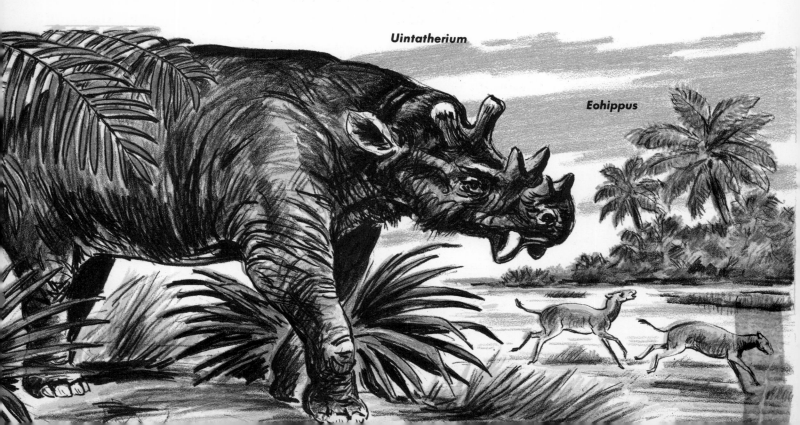

Uintatherium

Eohippus

Crocodile

REPTILE SURVIVORS

When a geologist called the close of the Mesozoic era "the time of the great dying," he did not refer only to the passing of the dinosaurs. This was a period when a wholesale disappearance of animal life took place. In the seas many invertebrates that had flourished for millions of years now vanished, as did the plesiosaurs and other reptiles that had returned to life in the water. The flying reptiles were no longer to be seen in the air, and on land the reign of the dinosaurs came to an end. Several different theories have been suggested as to why this all happened, but there are certain facts which must have had a bearing on the events. Gradually there became apparent a world-wide change in climate. No longer did even, tropical temperatures prevail far and wide; temperatures began to fluctuate between warm and cold in various zones. Also earth movements were upthrusting new mountain ranges, and swamps and palm-covered lowlands gave way to hills and valleys covered with hardwood trees. The adjustments necessary to survive such changes would indeed be great—but the mammals, birds, insects, and many other invertebrates succeeded. The dinosaurs and certain other fabulous reptiles did not; however, a few of the reptilian tribe showed that it could be done. They have survived to the present day!

47

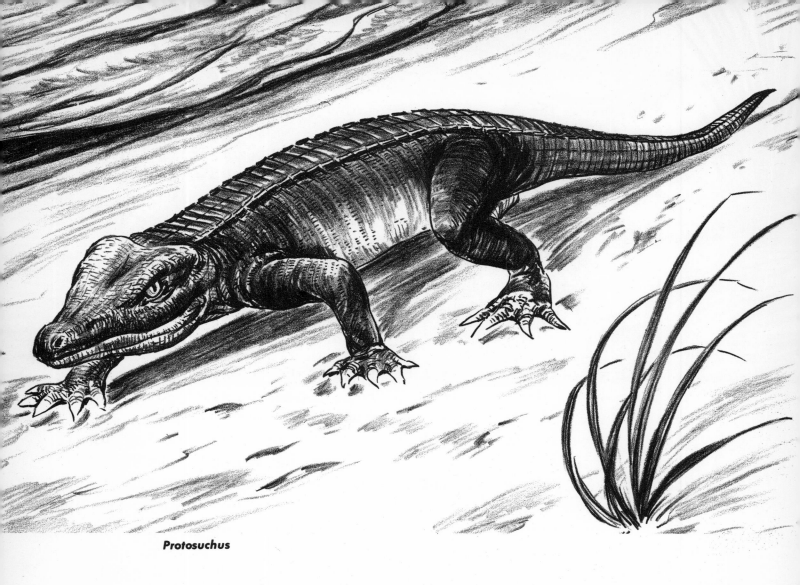

Protosuchus

The ancestry of the giant among the surviving reptiles—the crocodile—may be traced back to the early days of the Mesozoic era, when dinosaurs were becoming established. The first known "ancestor" was a small creature, about the dimensions of a medium-sized lizard. Though it was a close relative of the thecodonts (the remarkable two-legged reptiles that gave rise to the dinosaur tribe) it had features that were definitely crocodilian. On its back, belly, and around the tail were large, rectangular plates, forming a heavy armor. Its rather short head was made prominent by an elongated, pointed nose, and its eyes were of good size. The name given this forerunner of the crocodiles is *Protosuchus*.

Protosuchus was far from being a savage hunter, like the crocodiles of today. It was a harmless little one, doubtless anxious to keep out of the way of larger, meat-eating reptiles in spite of its heavy protective covering. But conditions favored its survival, and the crocodiles grew large and varied. By the Jurassic period crocodiles (considerably different from the ancestral type) were flourishing, some of them living in the open ocean, some along the seashore, and others in streams and lakes.

48

Still later in the Age of Reptiles, during the time *Tyrannosaurus* was coming into prominence on land, there was a second great period of growth among the crocodiles. By the end of the Mesozoic era the three groups that inhabit the earth today had appeared: those with a pointed snout, those having a broad snout which we call alligators, and the very narrow-snouted gavials. The crocodile that probably sets the size record for all time lived in the Cretaceous period. With good reason it was named *Phobosuchus* (*phobos* meaning "fear"; *souchos*, "crocodile"). Its length was something like fifty feet; its skull alone measured more than six feet in length and four feet in breadth. Equipped with cruel teeth and covered with heavy armor, this was an outstanding monster in a world devoted to monsters.

We have already met the turtles among the sea-dwelling animals that lived during the Mesozoic era. The first creature which somewhat suggested these tank-like reptiles, and which lived before the reptilian age began, is known by the name *Eunotosaurus*. This ancestral turtle had an arrangement of bones forming its spinal column that resembled the vertebrae of a turtle, and it also had ribs expanded to such an extent that they touched one another. Apparently this was a first step in the development of the turtle shell, which affords such great protection for the soft body.

Early in the Age of Reptiles true turtles had become well established, and from that time to the present day the remarkably constructed form has changed very little.

Most widely distributed of all reptiles in our modern world are the lizards and snakes. Since the snakes actually are a special kind of lizard, from which legs have disappeared, their original ancestry may be considered as merging into that of the lizards. The typical lizards, with elongated sprawling bodies, made their appearance in Jurassic times.

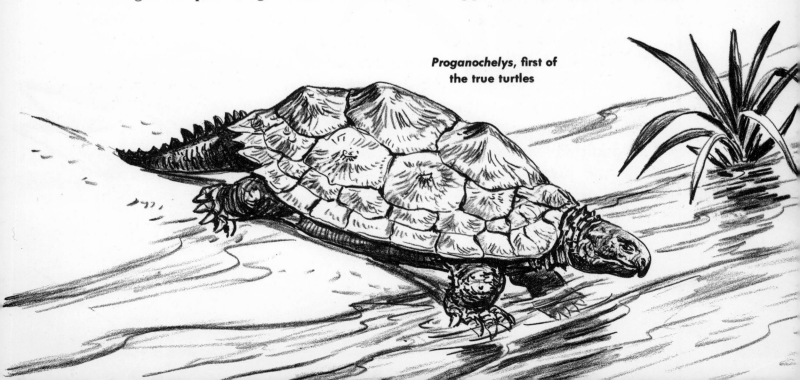

Proganochelys, first of the true turtles

Since then they have developed in a variety of forms and have managed to thrive in many kinds of surroundings, from seashore to desert, in tropical and temperate climes. Apparently the snakes, too, date from the Cretaceous period. Their success in survival is well known, for they may be found under all sorts of conditions, in every land except Ireland and the frozen ends of the earth.

Besides these common and widespread modern reptiles, there is one strange creature living on the rocky coasts of New Zealand that truly deserves the title "living fossil." Its popular name is "tuatara." The tuatara gives the impression of being just another lizard, but its internal structure reveals that it is a distinct type of reptile. It is the one and only survivor of a line that began when dinosaurs were coming into prominence. The scientific name for the tribe means "beak-head," for a distinguishing feature is a deep, beak-like formation at the front of the skull. Quite small in size, they are nevertheless definitely related to the dinosaurs. For this reason the little tuatara of New Zealand is a truly direct contact with the animals that were lords of the earth during the Age of Reptiles.

Tuatara

FOSSILS AND THEIR DISCOVERY

The Age of Reptiles ended some seventy million years ago, and as we have seen, many of the earth's leading citizens of that era disappeared completely. How then do we know about their existence? And how can anything be discovered about their ways of life? The key word in the answer to such questions is "fossils."

The term fossil is taken from a Latin word, *fossilis*, which originally was applied to anything dug out of the earth. However, this definition falls far short of explaining the true nature of fossils as we know them today. More exactly we may say a fossil is the remains of, or indications of, organisms that lived on earth in a past geologic age. Thus there are not only fossil bones, fossil shells, and fossilized wood, but fossil footprints and burrows. Sometimes a soft part of an animal, such as the skin, becomes fossilized, but this is unusual. Most fossils have been transformed into stone.

51

When we know what fossils are we still have cause to wonder how they can reveal events that took place before there were witnesses to record them. Fossils make it possible to unlock the door to the past, but behind that door is a time scale, worked out by scientists, on which the whole plot of the prehistoric story hangs. The time scale is based on the fact that the hard foundation of the earth is made up of layers belonging to various geologic ages and each having its own types of fossils—types that are not to be found in younger or older layers. With a thorough understanding of rocks and a knowledge of animal and plant life a scientist can, piece by piece, put the prehistoric "mystery" together. He has learned the best type of setting in which to look for fossils: they will never be in igneous or metamorphic rock, but in sedimentary types, such as limestone, sandstone, or shale, which are compressed bits of sediment. When a fossil is found, he must be able to identify it and to know how to compare it with other fossils.

Another cause for wonder is why, since it was possible for fossils to come into existence, fossil remains are not strewn more or less evenly over the whole earth. Why are they discovered only in certain areas? The explanation is that very special conditions must exist in order for fossilization to take place. As a rule, when an animal dies, bones as well as flesh decay and disappear. But should a creature die in a location where its body is soon covered by the mud of river or ocean bottom or by shifting desert sands, the body's decay is very slow. And if conditions are right, as the hard portions start to break down, the original material is replaced by mineral matter. Thus a fossil is created.

When a paleontologist goes hunting fossil vertebrates, his equipment includes whisk broom, paint brush, hammer, awl, pick ax, shellac, tissue paper, string, shovels, plaster of paris, and burlap. Dynamite sometimes is added to the "working tools" in case it is necessary to dislodge great masses of rock to uncover fossils. Usually the pick ax and hammer serve for this work, however. The awl and brush then help clear sand and dust from the discoveries. As the bones are uncovered they are given a coat of

shellac and covered with tissue paper so that air—reaching them for the first time after maybe millions of years—will not cause them to crumble. As further protection, each part of a skeleton is covered with strips of burlap that have been dipped in liquid plaster or flour paste. When the strips dry they hold the bones firmly, so they may be safely moved. The under part of the fossil is then given the same treatment the top and sides have received. A very large specimen is further safeguarded with sticks of wood, attached to it in the fashion of splints. The scientist excavating fossils does a careful job of making a chart which shows the exact position in which each bone was found. This is of great help later in the laboratory, where skeletons are pieced together.

Any single fossil discovery may be of real importance, a complete fossil skeleton probably is more so; but it is the bringing together of information about many, many fossils from all parts of the world that truly reveals facts about prehistoric times. As these facts are interpreted, the story comes to life—a story of events that date back to the long ago, when plants and animals were making quiet beginnings on a young planet, and continuing through the fantastic Age of Reptiles to the days when people began to record history in their own way.

54

Tyrannosaur   **Triceratops**

Index and Pronouncing Guide

ERAS	PERIODS	YEARS DURATION	DOMINANT ANIMAL LIFE
	Recent		
CENOZOIC	Pleistocene Pliocene Miocene Oligocene Eocene Paleocene	70 Million	
MESOZOIC (140 Million Years)	Cretaceous	60 Million	
	Jurassic	35 Million	
	Triassic	45 Million	
PALEOZOIC (350 Million Years)	Permian	25 Million	
	Carboniferous	50 Million	
	Devonian	65 Million	
	Silurian	75 Million	
	Ordovician	75 Million	
	Cambrian	90 Million	
PROTEROZOIC ARCHAEOZOIC AZOIC	1500 Million Years	No fossil records from these eras…